MOTION IN THE C

Wise Publications
part of The Music Sales Group
London / New York / Paris / Sydney / Copenhagen / Berlin / Madrid / Tokyo

Published by
Wise Publications
14-15 Berners Street, London, W1T 3LJ, UK.

Exclusive distributors:
Music Sales Limited
Distribution Centre, Newmarket Road,
Bury St Edmunds, Suffolk, IP33 3YB, UK.

Music Sales Pty Limited
120 Rothschild Avenue, Rosebery,
NSW 2018, Australia.

Order No. AM989307
ISBN 13: 978-1-84609-918-2
ISBN 10: 1-84609-918-8
This book © Copyright 2007 Wise Publications,
a division of Music Sales Limited.

Edited by Fiona Bolton.
Music arranged by Jack Long.
Music processed by Paul Ewers Music Design.

Original cover design & art direction by www.zipdesign.co.uk.
Photography & art direction by Ellis Parrinder at PCP.
Retouching by Jamie Currey.

Printed in the EU.

www.musicsales.com

WE ARE THE YOUNG

WORDS & MUSIC BY JAMES BOURNE, THOMAS FLETCHER, DANIEL JONES,
HARRY JUDD, DOUGIE POYNTER, JULIEN EMERY & JASON PERRY

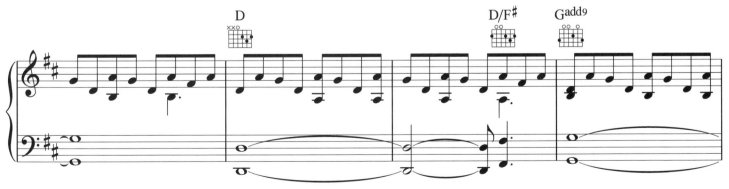

10

11

13

STAR GIRL

WORDS & MUSIC BY THOMAS FLETCHER, DANIEL JONES, HARRY JUDD,
DOUGIE POYNTER, DANIEL CARTER, JULIEN EMERY & JASON PERRY

Fly a-way;_____ watch the night_ turn in-to day;___

dance_ on the Mil-ky Way.___ Melt me with your

eyes. My_____ Star Girl rules the

sky._____

PLEASE, PLEASE

WORDS & MUSIC BY THOMAS FLETCHER,
DANIEL JONES, DOUGIE POYNTER & JASON PERRY

Original key B major.

22

To Coda

I wan-na get with you.

Please, please, Lind - say, please!

2. The sun sets the co-lour of fire;

your red hair

Lind - say, please!___

Please, please, Lind - say, please!___

Please,   please,

Lind - say,   please!___

Please,   please,   Lind - say;   please,   please,

Lind - say;   please,   please,   please,   please   me!

SORRY'S NOT GOOD ENOUGH

WORDS & MUSIC BY THOMAS FLETCHER, DANIEL JONES,
DOUGIE POYNTER, JULIEN EMERY & JASON PERRY

TRANSYLVANIA

WORDS & MUSIC BY THOMAS FLETCHER & DOUGIE POYNTER

Original key G♯m

BUBBLEWRAP

WORDS & MUSIC BY THOMAS FLETCHER

Original key Db major.

wish I could bub-ble - wrap my heart, in case I fall and

2. I'm a lit - tle dazed and con- fused; well, life's a bitch and

43

LONELY

WORDS & MUSIC BY JAMES BOURNE & THOMAS FLETCHER

Original key D♭

1. It's on-ly been a day, but it's like I can't go on.
2. Your stuff is in my house, so ma-ny things I can't ig-nore.

I just wan-na say, I nev-er meant to do you wrong.
Coats still on the couch, your pho-tos on my free-zer door.

LITTLE JOANNA

WORDS & MUSIC BY MATTHEW FLETCHER,
THOMAS FLETCHER, DANIEL JONES & DOUGIE POYNTER

Original key B major

FRIDAY NIGHT

WORDS & MUSIC BY THOMAS FLETCHER, DANIEL JONES, HARRY JUDD,
DOUGIE POYNTER, DANIEL CARTER, JULIEN EMERY & JASON PERRY

1. Sleep-ing through the day, 'cause I work all night. Get out the way, things are
(2.) walls are grow-ing ears, I'm pa-ra-noid. No need to fear what you

make it all to - geth - er. They're real - ly giv - ing me the eye.

D.S. al Coda ⊕ *Coda*

They come a - live when I work the nights. I guess I should-'ve seen the warn - ing signs.

rit.

69

WALK IN THE SUN

WORDS & MUSIC BY DANIEL JONES, JULIEN EMERY & JASON PERRY

Original key F♯ major

I'm just fol - low- ing___ the road_____ for a walk_ in___ the sun,_

___ for a walk_ in___ the sun.___

To Coda 1 ⊕

D.C. al Coda 1

⊕ *Coda 1*

___ Sit -ting and watch -ing the world_ go -ing by;_ is it true

72

when we die__ we go up__ to the sky,__ woah._____ Woah.__

__ So ma-ny things__ that I don't__ un-der-stand. Put my feet

__ in the sand__ when I'm walk-ing in__ the sun._____ Woah,__

_____ walk-ing in__ the sun._____

D.C. al Coda 2

Verse 4:

I wonder how they put a man on the moon.

I wonder what it's like up there.

I wonder if you'll ever sing this tune.

All I know is, the answer's in the air.

Verses 5 and 6:
Instrumental

HOME IS WHERE THE HEART IS

WORDS & MUSIC BY THOMAS FLETCHER,
DANIEL JONES & JASON PERRY

1. I'm a lov-er, not___ a fight-er;
2. We'll light a fire and write___ a son-net;

hold me close and I'll take___ you high-er than___
pin your hopes and your dreams___ up-on___ it now,

Now's your chance: think___ of your lov-ers; we are all sis-ters and broth-ers.

Instrumental

Home_____ is where the

start - ed,___ where we___ be - long.___

Where we___ be - long.___ Where we___ be - long.__

Where we___ be - long.___

DON'T STOP ME NOW

WORDS & MUSIC BY FREDDIE MERCURY